Make Music With

Supergrass

Complete Lyrics / Guitar Chord Boxes / Chord Symbols
Fifteen classic songs with a foreword by Stevie Chick

Published 2002

© International Music Publications Ltd
Griffin House 161 Hammersmith Road London W6 8BS England

Editor: Chris Harvey
Foreword: Stevie Chick
Design: Dominic Brookman
Music arranged and engraved by: Artemis Music Ltd
Cover Photograph: © 2002 Parlophone with kind permission
All other photography © 2002 Keiran Doherty, Patrick Ford & Mick Hutson / Redferns Music Picture Library

Foreword

"We're no more wild and sexy than anyone down the pub."
Gaz Coombes, *Melody Maker*, 1995

It takes a band of quite peculiar talent and charisma to straddle the perplexing chasm that lies between those kissing cousins 'rock' and 'pop'. A band like **Supergrass**.

They sprung like Jim Henson-engineered Bash Street Kids, young and free (and with their teeth nice'n'clean), grabbed Britpop by its antiquated Carnaby Street lapels and shook several shades of pop glory into it. They were cheeky little monkeys, hirsute and peppered with glitter and stardust, humping the charts till the charts could stand no more, heart-throbs for the girls'n'boys'n'girls who twirled across Camden dancefloors when the genre known as 'indie' made its boldest, brashest, FIRSTEST assault on the mainstream. They blew glorious raspberries at the blinkered reverence of their contemporaries and bared their behinds at craven idols of The Beatles and The Kinks and The Stones, taking what they wanted from these over -farmed sources and then adding the pranksterish zing of Madness, the glam-stomping 'grrrrr' of Slade, and a heap more classic rock'n'pop influences, till what remained was an exhilarating blur of surging rock'n'roll and colossal pop choruses (not to mention swooning swagger and enviable suss).

And then, when they'd had enough of that, they stopped, and retreated back to the chugging, organic rock'n'roll sound that was their essence, their base. What's more, they did so without diminishing their devoted following, transforming themselves from compelling dayglo pop gadabouts, into rootsy, rough-hewn rockers whose songs would live on in perpetuity, long after the flash-in-the-pan pop scene that'd ushered the band in had passed.

To the extent that, in 2002, as their fourth album is readied for general consumption, Supergrass hold an unusual place amongst their former contemporaries. Oasis have all but disgraced their early glimmers of promise with successive dadrock chundering; Blur have become the bandwagon-chasing art-rock pretenders they were always accused of; while the rest of the Britpop massive have faded into an ignominy somewhere between infamy and obscurity. Supergrass, however, remain intact. The tabloid ghouls have long since ceased stalking the hairy ones for their scandal sheets and gossip columns, but those same beacons of popular interest understand and respect the appeal Supergrass have for the world at large.

They've survived an awkward coming of age, the passage of time, the slings and arrows of outrageous pop fortune, their ingenuity lying in their very disingenuousness. Exploding upon the world, precocious and preciously youthful, with an album that giddily celebrated all that was carefree and glorious about the twilight moments of adolescence, they avoided the grislier aspects of the transfer from wide-eyed pop-kids to a band whose career promised more with every passing release.

They stopped playing the roles the media had assigned them and wriggled free of the limiting personae developed for them the minute they no longer suited. No longer *quite* so young, they are, however, freer than ever. **Strange Ones** indeed, but, eight years after their debut single, these kids are still **Alright**.

The story begins in Oxford, specifically the Wheatley Park Comprehensive school. It was there that drummer Danny Goffey and guitarist/vocalist Gaz Coombes, barely into their teens, started their band The Jennifers, with bassist Andy Davies and guitarist Nick Goffey, Danny's older brother. This wasn't Goffey's first foray into rock'n'roll - in primary school he'd been in a group called The Fallopian Tubes.

But, crucially, The 'Tubes never got signed to a nationally-prominent indie label. The Jennifers, however, were. Nude Records - a label who would soon garner fame from signing glam writhers Suede - added the seethingly youthful band to their roster. In 1992, when Coombes and Goffey were just 16 and 18, respectively (and Coombes was still at school), the label released The Jennifers' debut EP, **Just Got Back Today**. The release contained four self-written numbers by the band, ranging from the dreamy acoustic reveries of **Tomorrow's Rain**, to the squalling blues harmonica and guitar workout of the title track, to the punkier, more ragged **Danny's Song** and **Rocks and Boulders**, a perplexing batch of songs for a band who were perhaps better

placed, sonically, equidistant between their two deepest influences: The Beatles and Ride (The Jennifers' manager, Mark Taylor, worked with the Thames Valley dreamers).

Indeed, the four-piece's sound was very much indebted to the nascent indie-rock sound of the time, allying shoegazing's pedal-augmented psychedelia with the skinny grooves of 'baggy' - rock'n'roll that aped acid-house's rampant hedonism and unbroken funk. While the sound certainly rooted the band to their era, and also to the kind of ghetto-ised indie-rock culture that would never truly trouble the mainstream, it won them a loyal following in Oxford. One regular attendee of the band's local gigs, Mickey Quinn, would end up playing a major role in the future of Danny and Gaz (or Gareth, as he was then known).

But the humble fame and acclaim the band enjoyed wasn't enough to satisfy Nude Records, nor hold the band together. Receiving lukewarm reviews in the press, and hardly setting the charts alight, **Just Got Back Today** would be The Jennifers' sole release. A second EP was recorded and readied for despatch, but Nude got cold feet and shelved it. The blow was the last straw for the band, who subsequently split.

Presciently, mere weeks before the band's dissolution, Goffey had told Coombes that, should The Jennifers ever run aground on the rocks of pop misfortune, he'd still want to work with him. With this promise at the back of his mind, Gaz momentarily abandon indie-rock stardom for a short career of asking hungry Oxford suburbanites if they'd ever visited a Harvester before.

This interlude working at a local branch of the restaurant chain would yield more than essential pennies for the lupine-coiffeured frontman. For it was here that he began hanging out with Mickey Quinn, a fellow Wheatley Park graduate seven years Gaz's senior but very much on the same rockular page. The rabid rock-lover had served years in going-nowhere local bands and recording his own songs on rickety tapes at home. He had the talent and the enthusiasm and the spirit for rock'n'roll stardom. As yet, however, he hadn't discovered the perfect vehicle.

The duo's coffee-break discussions on rock'n'roll and related matters led to rehearsals and plans and nascent steps into the spotlight. Gaz enlisted Danny's aid, and the trio named themselves Theodore Supergrass, and then (in a rare flash of sanity), simply Supergrass. Their inaugural gig took place in a field besides Mickey's house. Their audience was a bemused herd of cows.

The band's next audience were only a tad less bovine, a flock of record industry A&R types swarming about the Jericho Tavern, their tastebuds tantalised by Supergrass's demo tape, produced in Sawmills Studios in Cornwall, where the band still record. Industry enthusiasm for the brattish flush of talent that surged forth that night would soon be echoed by that of the general public.

All teenagers get up to mischief. Few are immune to the attractions of illicit herbs (wink wink). And some are dumb/unlucky enough to be apprehended by the cops in the act of imbibing said smokables.

So runs the plotline of **Caught By The Fuzz**, Gaz Coombes' autobiographical tale of the long arm of the law reaching in and snatching a reefer from his lips, aged 15, before taking him down the station and revealing his wrongdoing to his embarrassed, enraged mother.

Caught By The Fuzz was the perfect choice for Supergrass's debut single. Lyrically, it was funny, cheeky, ribald and exuberant. "Caught by the fuzz / When I was still on the buzz" snaps Gaz, every inch the snotty loudmouthed brat ready to go toe to toe with the coppers if need be. But then the 'fuzz' begin to work their intimidatory ways, "'Who sold you the blow?'" they bark in Gaz's face, and you can just imagine the lamplight shone straight in Gaz's eyes, and the wizened, impatient coppers keying up the tension like wannabe Sweeney extras gone gonzo. Finally, the boys in blue defer to a dope deterrent a million times more forbidding - Mrs Gaz Sr. "Here comes my mum / She knows what I done" he gibbers, pale and panic-stricken... "'You've blackened our name,'" she bellows, "'Well you, you should be ashamed! If only your father could see you know / He'd break down and throw you out, I'm sure'" she snarls, and one can almost hear an imaginary belt loop being loosened for some form of corporal punishment, once the errant dope-fiend has been dragged home (ear first). Gaz later reported that his mum greeted her immortalisation in song with no little pride, telling her friends, "Listen to the third verse, that's when I appear!"

Musically, ...**Fuzz** was perfectly of its time. The year was 1994, and Britpop was still in the ascendance, as band after band of skinny, pale and interesting boys were rediscovering the pleasures of various waves of British-invasion rock'n'roll, be it Beatlesesque anthemicism, Kinks-y social comment, Who-flavoured auto destruction, or the ragin' raucousness of '77-era punk-rock. **Caught By The Fuzz** initially allies the band firmly in the latter camp, its opening chords a violent, thrumming riffage that echoes early Jam and, most obviously, Noise Annoys -era Buzzcocks. But Supergrass were no one-trick ponies... While the verses were metallic thrashes with snotty, tantrum-spat lyrics, the choruses were huge glorious crescendos, with the band snarling in a near-operatic style that was as effective as it was ridiculous, bringing home the fearsomely over-the-top manicness of Gaz's predicament. It was pop-brilliance, dallying with various familiar genres, finding each fits 'em perfectly, but crucially never sticking with one for any longer than they wished, an indicator towards the self-possession, the creativity and the writhing refusal of categorisation and predictability that would become Supergrass's hallmarks in later months and years.

The song - backed with **Strange Ones** and released on local label Backbeat in the August of 1994 - was a sensation the minute it hit the racks and radio waves. John Peel's support, on his influential Radio One show, helped the single sell out of its initial 1,000 copy print run in weeks, and the single won breathless plaudits from all corners of the music press, including Single Of The Week in both *Melody Maker* and *NME* in the very same week. As an introduction to the sound and spirit of Supergrass, it can't be beaten... The sense of musical playfulness, winking naughtiness, easy humour, full-on rockin' glam, and essential pop knack was audaciously on display.

Here was a band going somewhere, its scant two minutes seventeen declared. Somewhere very special indeed.

The buzz was almost instantaneous. The Record Biz sharks swum in close with a vengeance, though Danny and Gaz - still wary after their less-than-satisfactory experience in The Jennifers - warily held back from any offers until they were sure they weren't going to get bitten again. But, soon the band found themselves laying ink to paper and signing to Parlophone Records, making them cousins with Blur (who they'd soon support at an epochal Alexandra Palace gig), signed to Parlophone subsidiary Food Records. The following year, the boys would tell lusty tales of an EMI party where they got to rub shoulders - and other body parts - with Cliff Richard and Shampoo, amongst others.

But before the carnival of pop could begin, there was the matter of one further 'indie' release, a rather delectable slab of green vinyl on Backbeat Records which snuffled up any last remaining crumbs of doubt as to 'Grass's impending superstardom. The song was **Mansize Rooster**, and it plucked the trio from the grungey melee of guitars that characterised the **Caught By The Fuzz / Strange Ones** double whammy by dint of fairground piano, calamitous rock'n'roll riffage and yearning Bowie-esque glam sonics.

Mansize Rooster opens with a stomping rhythm and a rampantly grin-inducing see-saw piano ramble, Gaz singing sweetly and sincerely on the top... Until the chorus kicks in, that is, with a signature Danny Goffey drum-tumble and the electric guitars kicking in. From this point on, Gaz is yowling lustily and slamming lithe guitar hooks into the mix, the whole effect akin to a rollercoaster lurching into nosebleed velocity at the drop of a pin, until the chorus hits the wall that is the rinky dink verse, with Coombes yelling, through an echo-laden microphone in the background, "Rooooostah!". Repeat this process again, and you have this amazing single, save for the last-breath coda, setting the breakneck chorus into one last dervish, Gaz and Mick and Danny laying down some rocktastically Pete Townsend-esque crescendos. It was the sound of The Who roughing up Bowie in the nutty music-hall of Madness's dreams, and its gloriously dayglo technicolour stomp-pop trumped even the grintastic **Caught By The Fuzz** for audacity, verve and glee. This was pop music so laden down with energy and gimmicks and unforgettable melodies it was forever in danger of collapsing with its own ingenuity. But somehow, it all held together.

When a rejigged version of the song hit the shelves as a single, after the band's transfer to Parlophone, the sleeve tagged it "More 'Cock' than 'Doodle-Do'". As press hysteria surrounding the band grew, the band's good looks soon became a subject as worthy of discussion as the band's music in profiles. Well, this was a key transitionary era for indie-pop, in the past the preserve of awkward-cute frontmen, characterised by the twisted handsomeness of a Steven Morrissey, or the clunky geeky charm of Wedding Present's David Gedge. But, with Britpop, indie-pop was turning up any number of heart-throbs who could snatch the genre coverage in pop-rags like *Smash Hits* as surely as the overwrought inkies, *Melody Maker* and *NME*, that were usually their preserve.

There was the elfin-pretty Damon Albarn, all mockney wink and girlish green eyes. There was the troglodyte Liam Gallagher, stirring unspoken homosexual feelings amongst Oasis' laddish male throngs, and quickening the heartbeats of their female fandom. There was Pulp's Jarvis Cocker, the thinking indie-chick's bit of polyester charity shop-chic crumpet, plus a wave of lower-tier indie lookers, a tad generic in their ruffled-hair, adidas tops and trainers, and deep-blue Levis.

And then there was Supergrass. There was something alluringly odd and

oddly alluring about these boys from the start. One's eyes was instantly drawn to Gaz's lycanthrope visage - severe sideburns curving up his cheekbones like he were Wolverine from the comic-book *X-Men*, matching his slicing eyebrows - but Quinn and the baby-faced Goffey were striking too. What's more, their early interviews saw some of the music press's more lucid and incisive interviewers drawing brilliantly funny and candid dialogues from the boys, as they coasted along one of the most impressive and extreme waves of popularity Britpop had yet countenanced. Tales of excess involving groupies and booze and drugs were par for the course, though already there was a sneaking suspicion that the band might rather chat about their music than the hair-raising derring-do they were getting up to after the shows. A sense that, perhaps, these personae were growing at expense to their music.

But this wasn't the time yet to give free reign to such anxieties. No, this was the time for the band to hunker down and record their debut album.

I Should Coco is still, years after the fact, a dizzyingly confident, brilliant debut album, stretching all the inspiration and genius and exhilaration of the band's early singles over forty or so minutes of woozy psychedelia, rushing mod freakbeat, punk-angled rave-ups, and deftly-sequinned pop twists. Perfectly paced, it doesn't let-up once; even its 'throwaway' tune, the helium-hyped **We're Not Supposed**, has a cheeky charm that fits in with the album's overall tone of random hi-jinks and raucous knockabouts.

The sense is of a party ever at the edge of boiling over into a messy brawl, but somehow maintaining this air of breakneck, loose-limbed abandon throughout. Invention and inspiration are brazenly peppered throughout, but nothing is too showy, too obvious. The back sleeve captures the trio as the perfect heart-throbs for their era, wearing cheap-ish down-to-earth casual clothes, sweaty, pressed up against a graffitti-clad dressing room wall (doubtless post-gig). Danny's clasping a bottle of beer and his arm's draped across Mick's shoulder; Gaz leans wastedly against his sticksman. The air is one of loose bonhomie, unassuming swagger. There's something to proven here, sure, but Supergrass know the slab of vinyl contained within the sleeve has done just that, and a lot more...

Danny barks out the count-in and clicks sticks in the opening seconds, before the claustrophobic garage-gallop of **I'd Like To Know** - all frantic farfisa squelches, corrugated guitar growl and phased blasts of colour - kicks in. **Caught By The Fuzz** cuts in next, in barely the flash of a lighter-flint, before the head-spinning rockage gives way to the sunsplash plink-plonk of **Mansize Rooster**. Your head is spinning, your heart is racing, you my well have broken a sweat. This, you marvel, must be one of the greatest open 1-2-3s in pop history.

Easy tiger. Supergrass manage to maintain this hit-rate all the way through the first side of the album, each cut an absolute, unabashed classic. Catch your breath, because the band's signature tune, and the song that'll probably follow them to the grave (not to mention the theme tune whose caricature of youthful abandon precipitated the changes that would follow **I Should Coco**) is about to begin.

Alright snatched Supergrass from indie-pop superstars to genuine pop stars in a flash. And why not? Its irresistible pop quality remains unsullied by repeated plays, its anthemic embrace of an entire generation's sense of youthful ease and irresponsibility leaving intact its winning sense of oddness. Wrecklessness and restlessness are the keys here, "Sleep around / If we like," "Smoke a fag / Put it out," "Had a roll / hit a wall" sings Gaz, detailing all manner of vacant silliness, easy good times and thoughtless activity, each time with the payoff, "But we're alright"... But in the chorus lies a twist, a gorgeous little vignette of love from afar, a little crease of uncertainty and seductive mystery: "Have you seen, as she turns / we are strange in our worlds". This 'strangeness', and its very attractiveness are key to the album, popping up also in **I'd Like To Know** ("I'd like to know where the strange ones go") and the eponymous **Strange Ones**; this sense of odd allure, of inviting mystery. Given the band's milieu and context, its hard not to imagine that attraction being the transgressive activities the rock'n'roll life offers - drugs, excess, sex - treated here as innocent diversions, beckoning from across the muddy festival fields, the very optimism in the songs mirroring the wave of hedonism Britpop ushered into the previously angsty cloisters of indie-pop. (The angst would raise its head in the following track, **Lose It**). In Supergrass's hands, this is a very seductive concept indeed.

The music perfectly accented the brazenly upbeat lyrics. An incessantly grinning piano line runs throughout, an inverse of the menacing one-note wail John Cale laid through The Stooges' seminal **I Wanna Be Your Dog** (again, **Lose It** would reflect a Stoogian influence on the 'Grass's rockout side), fittingly, since **Alright** is in content the inverse to '...Dog"s existential torpor. The almost-jazzy, gentle guitar slashes throughout similarly help to cultivate a summery-feel - the song was tailor made for that carefree season. Moreover,

the tight, melodic guitar solo after the second chorus is straight out of Radio 2. While there's no obvious layer of irony, sarcasm or cynicism to the track, it does have the faint air of a twisted sense of forced-glee, akin to The Specials' later underscoring of ska's upbeat skank with layers of social dread. Or maybe Alright *is* simply a shallow paean to shallow pleasures; it is still sublime in its evocation thereof.

The following Lose It was the flip of the coin, dark heavy and nasty. Little wonder grunge label 'Sub Pop' pressed it up as a seven-inch in the States. Lenny continued the heavier guitar thrum, while lightening the atmosphere a tad. The revving, raring to go opening passage, not to mention the limber rockouts that peppered the song, recall the Jimi Hendrix Experience's sense of hyped-up R'n'B; Supergrass may have lacked Jimi's visionary guitar work, but Goffey and Quinn matched Noel Redding and Mitch Mitchell's fluid, flowing and frantic rhythm section, all bass-runs and drum fills ago-go. And so ended one of the most stunning, flawless first-sides in rock.

So side two opened with tape-speed japery and the manic psyche-punk rush of Strange Ones, before sequeing into the breakneck thrash of Sitting Up Straight. A sequel of sorts to Alright, this song again harks back to the simplicity of youth, this time allying the freewheeling rockout of the music to a gorgeous lyric which has Gaz gazing upon the a boy smoking on the bus, mixing images of the transient perfections of single moments ("Evening time turns to dusk" he notes) with talk of escapism, and Gaz's identification with this yearning to free himself from the daily grind. It last two minutes, but it lingers.

And so begins a gentler patch of perfection: the woozy seduction-blues of She's So Loose, all mysteries and weird chord-changes; the winningly oddball We're Not Supposed To; the nudgingly poignant dadrock of Time; the wistful carnival psychedelia of Sofa (Of My Lethargy). All build up to the deliciously slight, moving Time To Go. "Who could ask for more?" questions Gaz, over sweet, jaunty guitar strums. It's the perfect end to an album which feels like a scrapbook evocation of the flash of freedom, experimentation and discovery which is adolescence. Made all the more exquisite by the sense of its own very transience.

The pacing of I Should Coco is flawless. Opening with the early singles, it charts the already-skyrocketing development and maturation of the band; as tracks like Alright seem to anticipate the passing of the heady abandon that characterises Caught By The Fuzz, so Time To Go is nothing less than a lament for that very period, and a signal that it is well and truly passed.

"Thanks to everyone for everything you've done / But now it's time to go / Who could ask for more?"

Who indeed?

"(Earlier, on the tour bus, the first word which comes out of the speakers when the CD player is switched on is 'cocaine'. Spooky. Or perhaps not so when you consider this band listen to JJ Cale and the truly atrocious Frank Zappa's Dinah Mo Hum for *pleasure*.)"
- Everett True, *Melody Maker*, 1995

"Yeah," says Danny, "with Alright it was every flippin' bus driver going: 'Awright son? How are you then? Awright?' Didn't get that with 'Going Out', though. Didn't get: 'Awright? Going Out are ya?'"
Vox Magazine, 1997

As the band rode the hurricane of success that I Should Coco ushered in, as that very hurricane became tiresome to them, as their personae of gadding youths and carefree caricatures began to fit them less well, as media hysteria over the kids grew to freakish levels, as Supergrass became less about their music and more about their interview questions and their zeitgeist-snaffling videos, as Steven Spielberg reportedly planned a Monkees-esque TV series based on the three-piece fercrissakes, there was a sense that something was gonna give in the Supergrass camp.

Danny and Mick had both become fathers in the period directly following I Should Coco. Gaz, meanwhile, had become the focus of media attention for the band, his decision to cut his long hair back to a suedehead cut filling many columns in the youth-hungry tabloids. It was an uncomfortable position. Even their full-time bonhomie and commendable abuse of the record industry's corporate hospitality had soured, as the band noted that they no

longer enjoyed getting fucked up on Parlophone's tab, as, they declared, "the music industry's full of wankers".

What's more, **Alright** had swiftly become an anvil around their necks. It had taken the band into the mainstream, but the 'Grass soon learnt the general public's perception of the band was limited to Gaz's hirsute appearance and 'THAT' song. Swiftly recognising they were being painted into a corner, and perhaps sensing the pressure of following up such a zeitgeist-possessing album (and also, no doubt, aware that the Britpop dream had soured into a laddish glut of average guitars and lesser tuneage), the band elected for something of an image re-invention for their next album, in addition to a return to the musical essence that ushered in the head-spinning pop-rock brilliance of **I Should Coco**.

We're **Only In It For The Money** ran the title of Supergrass's sophomore album, and the sleeve featured the band dressed up as ragged ne'erdowells, busking in grainy sepia like depression-era vagabonds. The kids in this vignette weren't young, and didn't look like they kept their teeth nice'n'clean. But, after the dust settled, after the music-press fever surrounding the release died down, after skeptics ceased crowing over the album's 'disappointing' sales in comparison to **I Should Coco**, it soon became apparent the band had freed themselves from their troubling iconic status.

The image in **...Money** was usurped by the music. In interviews since halfway through the **Coco** promotional tour, the band had been citing the deeply-unfashionable sources that were inspiring their music, rootsy rockers like J J Cale, whose shuffling boogie-rock became a heavy influence on critical bete noirs like Eric Clapton and Mark Knopfler. While Supergrass were unlikely to indulge in dozy Delta blues workouts and tedious triple-guitar wankathons for balding, ponytailed yuppies, citing Cale as a source was a distinct gesture towards erasing the image that had dogged them since **Alright**.

In the interim, the band had also changed their lineup slightly. The last tours promoting **I Should Coco** had featured the band augmented by a horn section, almost de rigeur at the height of Britpop (Blur were also found of a touch of brass back in the day). But the band felt that the addition damaged the tight, furious power of their three-piece lineup; in their place in future would sit Gaz's older brother Rob on keyboards, an enigmatic figure who shied away from interviews, but nevertheless helped pen many of Supergrass's tunes from hereon in.

The first single off **In It For The Money** defiantly rung the changes for the 'Grass. **Going Out** was characterised by a surging, psychedelic fairground motif, set off by wickedly piquant harmonies, a rage of tie-dyed bristle that sounded like an echo direct from Haight-Ashbury. So far, so Supergrass (though the psychedelia here is of a stronger and more pungent yield than, say, **Sofa (Of My Lethargy)**. But the lyrics seem to herald a more publicity-unfriendly 'Grass, wary and almost cynical. "If you wanna go out," sings Gaz, "Read it in the papers / Tell me what it's all about". No more seeing friends or seeing the sights, this was Supergrass as super-psyche shut-ins.

The raucous Supergrass rockouts of yore were revisited for **Richard III**, the second single off the album, but again this single marked out the 'new' sound of the 'Grass: like before, but *more*. Squalling, raging guitars revved at full volume as a strangulated Gaz yells above the din and melee, the riffs lacing together like stormclouds gathering in the sky. This was no joke, this was rock'n'roll, and Supergrass were living up to their feral iconography, while further trampling on their perceived comic book personae.

The next single, **Sun Hits The Sky**, was a return to the more gleeful and upbeat Supergrass sound, however. A slight, delicious melody rings through the song, as Gaz sings of a place where the sun hits the sky, the chorus revealing what could easily be interpreted as a drug-referencing lyric, "I am a doctor, I'll be your doctor / I'm on my way, you won't come down today".

The album itself maintained the air of acid-tinged lyrical playfulness and witheringly majestic psychedelia, toying with the band's previous incarnation as grinning popstar monkeyboys with a knowingness that tempered what could have been the usual sour sarcasm that tinges many post-first taste of success releases by young bands.

The title track was the most explicitly satirical tune. Gaz's vocals are the standout here, ekeing out the snakey melody over a backing track of soaring pomp and brilliance. "Here I see a time, to go and leave it all behind" he sings in the opening line, referencing perhaps the band's decision to ditch the madness of the **...Coco** era, but swiftly Gaz lurches into the recurring lyrics of the song, "Got my mind made up I got my finger on the button going way home / Got the sun turned down got a feeling in my pocket going way home", balanced out by the romantic counter-line "But all I can see is our love and all I can hear is her". Is it a comment on the band's need for money, post-parenthood, an apologia for rock-as-career? If so, the band needn't have bothered, since **In It For The Money** is as glorious a tune as Supergrass have ever conjured. More likely, its a sarcastic retort to sour critics who might be chiding the band for resting on their laurels, yet another unfounded accusation, since the 'Grass were stretching perceptions every which way with the album's diesel-powered psychedelia.

But moments of introspection also coloured the album, like the lush **It's Not Me**, seductive wah-wah guitar layered over caressing acoustic lines. In the song, Gaz confronted the aftermath of success and conflicts of identity in some of his most honest and open lyrics yet. "Over their heads I find a place to crawl away," he sings. "I try to find my piece of mind / But I know what I miss / Now it's gone".

Late In the Day is perhaps the apex of this trend, again stripped bare to the sparsest of instrumentation. The star here is Gaz's keening vocals, beautifully produced, ekeing out the melodies with tenderness and sensitivity. The quantum leap between this performance and, say, **Caught By The Fuzz**'s exhilarating but strictly one-paced spirit. Supergrass were maturing with grace.

The album would feature one last dig at the furore that greeted **...Coco**, however. The blissful soft-rock of **You Can See Me** is matched powerfully to Gaz's pleading, embittered vocal. "If you like me / You can buy me and take me home," he sings, commenting on the commodification of his existence, post-stardom. "All the crazies / try to space me but I don't know" he adds, like Woody Allen circa Stardust Memories staring out at his fans through a fish-eyed lens. The distorted existence of the pop star is compounded by the chorus: "You can't see me / I'm not really there".

"I saw Del Amitri on *Top Of The Pops* the other day. The sideburns, that drummer. It looked like us in ten years' time."
Danny Goffey to *Select* Magazine, 1998

Gaz: "I mean, we do want a long career - we don't wanna go back on the dole if we can help it, y'know! But that doesn't mean you have to turn into the Stones."
Mickey: "We're a real band though."
Gaz: What, like instead of a cardboard band? What the f*** does that mean?
Mickey: "Well, not like Take That or whatever."
from an interview with *Melody Maker*'s Taylor Parkes, 1995

But, crucially, **Supergrass** had pulled it off, paying pop at their own rules and succeeding, without having to play the teen simian freak card to score success in both the charts and the reviews.

In the period between **In It For The Money** and its follow-up, Gaz and Mick got to collaborate with their hero, gumbo-blues figurehead Dr John, for his album **Anutha Zone**. Meanwhile, Danny teamed up with his partner Pearl for the indie-allstar Lodger project, garnering much acclaim and cult success.

1999 saw Supergrass's thrid album, a logical continuation of 'In It for The Money''s progression. For the sleeve, the band's visages were superimposed over images of their skeletons; the title was, simply, Supergrass. The stripped-down concept begun with the preceding record was played up to the full here; this was Supergrass, naked and shorn of pretence and fakery and gimmicks. And it was brilliant.

The two songs from Supergrass contained in this volume earmark the two extremes the band were excelling at this point. **Moving** was Supergrass's newfound tender side in exclesis... Opening with swirling and chiming acoustic guitars, it featured possibly Gaz's sweetest vocals yet, keening like Jeff Buckley but still possessed of his own identity.

After the lush, graceful intro follows the surging rock groove at the song's core. Again, the lyrics are somewhat bleak, concerning a loss of direction, a certain existential coldness. "Moving, just keep moving / Till I don't know what's sane", sings Gaz, in the opening lines. "Got a low, low feeling around me / And a stone cold feeling inside" he continues, in the chorus. This deliciously anthemic blast of melancholia is perhaps one of Supergrass's less-likely classics, but **Moving** soon became beloved of the nation, and a radio favourite.

Pumping On Your Stereo, however, proved that Supergrass could have their cake and eat it too. The audacity of the band to release a single so clearly designed to hang on the radiowaves like **Alright** did a scant few years ago, geed up with the kind of video that restored the band to the kind of larger-than-life caricatures they'd purposefully shunned in recent times.

Hooking up with the Jim Henson Studios, responsible of course for the Muppets amongst other fuzzy monstrous puppet exercises, the clip portrayed Supergrass as humoungously-limbed freakish beasts, thrumming their instruments like tartrazine-addled punkas. The band contributed the perfect soundtrack for the ramalama video, a slice of T-Rextasy, all glammy riffing and salacious vocals and nagging singalong lyrics. But again, there's a darker undertone to the tune than the simple optimism of, say, **Sitting Up Straight**. "The wider your eyes, the bigger the lies, yes it's true" sings Gaz, and he might well be singing about the duplicitous music industry. As he howls "You're all alone on the road / Well you'll burn all your bridges down / And now you're losing control", the sense of Gaz lamenting the detatchment of the rock'n'roll lifestyle is palpable. It's the same old Supergrass magic, only darker and deeper.

Supergrass' fourth album, **Life On Other Planets** promises to be a further chapter in the development of a band who, somehow, managed to have it all, so soon, and yet also pull back from the madness and all the distractions so they could develop on their own terms, in their own time.

For all their influences and acknowledged heroes, Supergrass are their own band. Era and genre can't possess them, and while they've been fashionable, they're not of any single fashion. This is their past, fifteen compelling reasons why you shouldn't take your eyes or ears off their future.

Stevie Chick has been a freelance music writer for four years, contributing to **Melody Maker, NME, Kerrang!, The Times,** the **Evening Standard** and **Sleaze Nation,** and is currently a contributing editor of **Careless Talk Costs Lives.** He lives in London and has recently completed work on his book **Don't Stop Now: The Ballad Of Guided By Voices,** the amazing tale of 30-something songwriter Robert Pollard's ascent from school teacher obscurity to indie-rock superstardom.

Discography:Albums

I Should Coco

I'd Like To know
Caught By The Fuzz
Mansize Rooster
Alright
Lose It
Lenny
Strange Ones
Sitting Up Straight
She's So Loose
*We're Not Supposed To
Time*
Sofa (Of My Lethargy)
Time To Go

Release Date: May 1995
Highest Chart Position: 1
Weeks On Chart: 36

In It For The Money

In It For The Money
Richard III
Tonight
Late In The Day
G Song
Sun Hits The Sky
Going Out
It's Not Me
Cheapskate
You Can See Me
Hollow Little Reign
Sometimes I Make You Sad

Release Date: April 1997
Highest Chart Position: 2
Weeks On Chart: 25

Supergrass

Moving
Your Love
What Went Wrong (In Your Head)
Beautiful People
Shotover Hill
Eon
Mary
Jesus Came From Out Of Space
Pumping On Your Stereo
Born Again
Faraway
Mama & Papa

Release Date: September 1999
Highest Chart Position: 3
Weeks On Chart: 14

Life On Other Planets

Za
Rush Hour Soul
Seen The Light
Brecon Beacons
Can't Get Up
Evening Of The Day
Never Done Nothing Like That Before
Funniest Thing
Grace
LA Song
Prophet 15
Run

Release Date: September 2002
Highest Chart Position: unknown
at time of publication
Weeks On Chart: unknown
at time of publication

Discography:Singles

Caught By The Fuzz
b/w *Strange Ones*
Release Date: August 1994
Highest Chart Position: n/a

Mansize Rooster
b/w *Sitting Up Straight*
Release Date: October 1994
Highest Chart Position: n/a

Caught By The Fuzz
b/w *Strange Ones, Caught By The Fuzz*
(acoustic)
Release Date: October 1994
Highest Chart Position: 43
Weeks On Chart: 2

Mansize Rooster
b/w *Sitting Up Straight, Odd*
Release Date: February 1995
Highest Chart Position: 20
Weeks On Chart: 3

Lenny
b/w *Wait For The* Sun*, Sex!*
Release Date: May 1995
Highest Chart Position: 10
Weeks On Chart: 3

Alright / Time
b/w *Condition, Je Suis Votre Papa Sucre*
Release Date: July 1995
Highest Chart Position: 2
Weeks On Chart: 10

Going Out
b/w *Melanie Davis, Strange Ones* (live)
Release Date: February 1996
Highest Chart Position: 5
Weeks On Chart: 6

Richard III
b/w *Sometimes I Make You Sad, Sometimes
We're Very Sad*, Nothing More's Gonna Get
In My Way, *20ft Halo*
Release Date: March 1997
Highest Chart Position: 2
Weeks On Chart: 5

Sun Hits The Sky
b/w *Some Girls Are Bigger Than Others, Sun
Hits The Sky* (Evening Session version)
Release Date: June 1997
Highest Chart Position: 10
Weeks On Chart: 4

Late In The Day
b/w *We Still Need More Than Anyone Can
Give, It's Not Me* (demo)*, Don't Be Cruel,
The Animal*
Release Date: October 1997
Highest Chart Position: 18
Weeks On Chart: 4

Pumping On Your Stereo
b/w *You'll Never Walk Again, Sick, What A
Shame, Lucky (No Fear)*
Release Date: May 1999
Highest Chart Position: 11
Weeks On Chart: 7

Moving
b/w *You Too Can Play Alright, Believer,
Faraway* (Acoustic)
Release Date: September 1999
Highest Chart Position: 9
Weeks On Chart: 5

Mary
b/w *Pumping on Your Stereo, Strange Ones,
Mary, Richard III, Sun Hits The Sky* (all live)
Release Date: November 1999
Highest Chart Position: 36
Weeks On Chart: 3

Never Done Nothing Like That Before
(limited edition 7")
Release Date: July 2002
Highest Chart Position: n/a

Grace
b/w *Tishing In Windows (Kicking Down
Doors), That Old Song*
Release Date: September 2002
Highest Chart Position: 13
Weeks On Chart: Unknown at time of
publication

Alright

Words and Music by
GARETH COOMBES, MICHAEL QUINN and DANIEL GOFFEY

D   Em7   F♯m   F

A7   G   Dm7   Em

♩ = 140

Intro D

4/4 | / / / / | / / / / | / / / / | / / / / | / / / / |

Verse 1 | D | | | |

We are young, we run green, keep our teeth nice and clean,   see our

Em7 | | D | |

friends, see the sights,   feel all right.   We wake up,

| | | | |

we go out, smoke a fag,   put it out,   see our

Em7 | | D | |

friends, see the sights,   feel all right.

Chorus 1   F♯m | | F | |

Are we like you?   I can't be sure   of the scene

Em7 | | A7 | |

as she turns.   We are strange in our world, but we are young,

Verse 2 | D | | | |

we get by,   can't go mad,   ain't got time, sleep a-

Em7 | | D | |

round   if we like, but we're all right.   Got some

| | | |

cash, bought some wheels,   took it out 'cross the fields lost control,

Em7 | | D | |

hit a wall,   but we're all right.

11

Chorus 2
     F#m | | F | |

       Are we like you?   I can't be sure   of the scene

     Em⁷ | | A⁷ | |

       as she turns   We are strange in our world, but we are young,

Interlude 1
  D | | | |

       we run green, keep our teeth nice and clean   see our

     Em⁷ | | D | |

     friends, see the sights,   feel all right.

Instrumental
  G   Dm⁷   G   F

| / / / / / | / / / / / | / / / / / | / / / / / |

  G   Dm⁷   G   F

| / / / / / | / / / / / | / / / / / | / / / / / |

  Em   A⁷

| / / / / / | / / / / / |

  D

| / / / / / | / / / / / | / / / / / | / / / / / |

  Em⁷   D   *(two guitars)*

| / / / / / | / / / / / | / / / / / | / / / / / |

| / / / / / | / / / / / | / / / / / | / / / / / |

  Em⁷   D

| / / / / / | / / / / / | / / / / / | / / / / / |

Chorus 3
     F#m | | F | |

       Are we like you?   I can't be sure   of the scene

     Em⁷ | | A⁷ | |

       as she turns   We are strange in our world, but we are young,

Interlude 2 D | | | |

we run green, keep our teeth nice and clean   see our

Em⁷ | | **D** | |

friends, see the sights,   feel all right.

Coda D

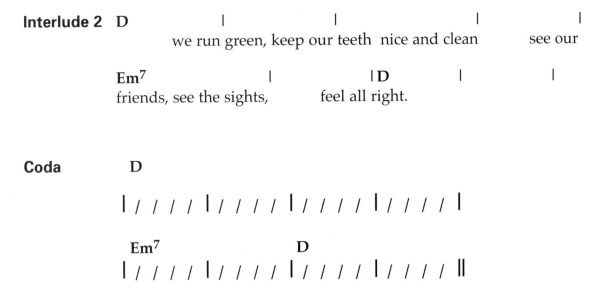

Em⁷ **D**

Caught By The Fuzz

Words and Music by
GARETH COOMBES, MICHAEL QUINN AND DANIEL GOFFEY

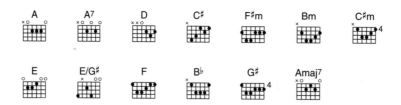

♩ = 156

Intro   A

4/4 | / / / / | / / / / | / / / / | / / / / |

| / / / / | / / / / | / / / / | / / / / |

Verse 1   A⁷ | D | C♯ | F♯m |
Caught by the fuzz, well I was   still on a buzz

A⁷ | D | C♯ | F♯m |
In the back of the van with my head in my hands

A⁷ | D | C♯ | F♯m |
Just like a bad dream, I was   only fifteen

Chorus 1   Bm | C♯m |
If only my brother could be here now   he'd

F♯m   E | D |
get me out and sort me out alright   I

                        | E | A | |
know I should have stayed at home tonight

Verse 2   A⁷ | D | C♯ | F♯m |
Locked in a cell,   feeling unwell,

A⁷ | D | C♯ | F♯m |
I talked to a man,   he said, 'It's better to tell.

A⁷ | D | C♯ | F♯m |
Who sold you the blow?' 'Well it was no-one I know.'   'If

14   © 1994 EMI Music Publishing Ltd, London WC2H 0EA

Chorus 2   Bm | C#m |
only you'd tell us, we'd let you go,   We'll

                F#m   E | D |
make it hard for you my son, so tell us what you know. We'll

                                 | E |
make you wish you'd stayed at home tonight'

Interlude   F#m | E/G# | D | E |
Ooh   *wah   ooh*   *wah*

                  F | B♭   E | A | |
ooh.

                  F#m | E/G# | D | E |
Ooh   *wah   ooh*   *wah*

                  F | B♭   E | A | |
ooh.

Verse 3   A⁷ | D |
Here comes my mum,   well she

                  C# | F#m |
she knows what I've done

                  A⁷ | D |
'Just tell them the truth,

                  C# | F#m   G#5 |
you know where it's from

                  A⁷ | D |
you've blackened our name, well you,

                  C# | F#m |
you should be ashamed.   If

Chorus 3   Bm | C#m |
only your father could see you now,   he'd

                  F#m   E | D |
break down, and he'd throw you out for sure   I

                                 | E |
never should have let you out tonight'

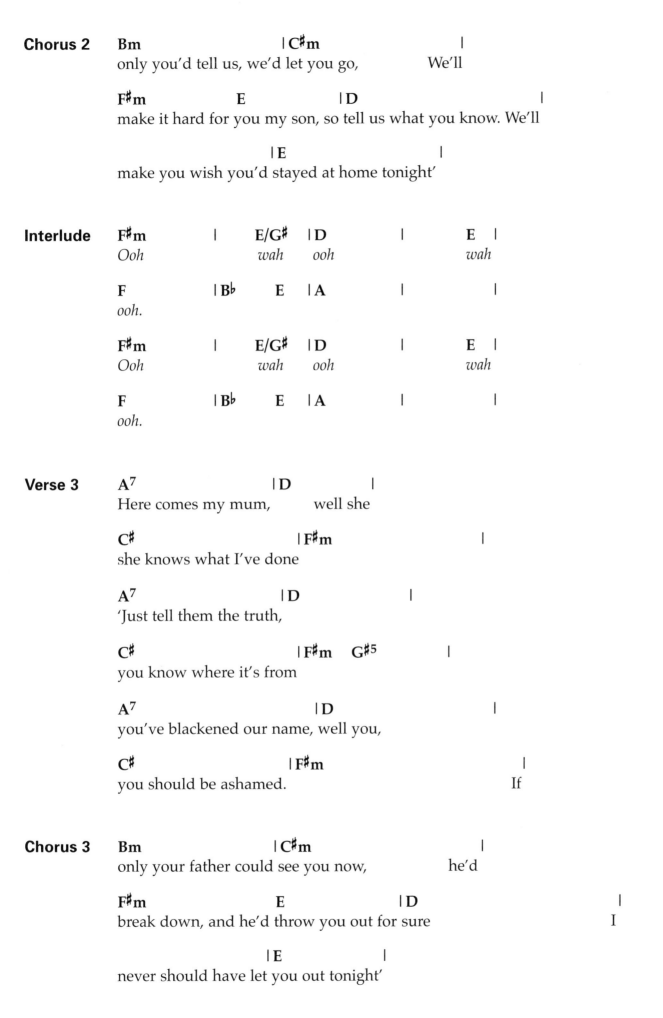

Coda   A | |
Tonight, tonight, *tonight*, tonight,

Aᵐᵃʲ⁷ | |
Tonight, tonight, *tonight*, tonight,

A | |
Tonight, tonight, *tonight*, tonight,

Aᵐᵃʲ⁷ | | A   ‖
Tonight, tonight, *tonight*.

Going Out

Words and Music by
GARETH COOMBES, MICHAEL QUINN, DANIEL GOFFEY AND ROBERT COOMBES

A D G D/A D/G Cmaj7 E7

Em7/B Bb Fmaj7 E B9sus4 Eb Bm7

♩ = 96

Intro

| A | D G | A | D G | | D G | A | D G |
| / / / / | / / / / | / / / / | / / / / |

4/4 | / / / / | / / / / | / / / / | / / / / |

| A | D/A | A | D/A | A | D/A | A | D/A |
| / / / / | / / / / | / / / / | / / / / |

Verse 1

A   D   G |A   D   G |
If you want to go out

A   D   G |A   D   G |
if you want to go out

Cmaj7 |E7 |
read it in the papers, tell me what it's all about,

A   D/A   D/G |A   D/A D/G |
yeah

Verse 2

A   D/A   D/G |A   D/A   D/G |
If you want to stay   home

A   D/A   D/G |A   D/A   D/G |
if you want to stay   home

Cmaj7 |E7 |
freedom of the papers, all you ever need to know

A   D/A   D/G |A   D/A D/G |
yeah.

Cmaj7 |E7 |
Freedom of the papers, all you've got to do, oh

Fmaj7 | G |
no, no, oh

A D/A D/G | A D/A D/G |
no.

Verse 3

A D/A D/G | A D/A D/G |
If you want to play home,

A D/A D/G | A D/A D/G |
if you want to play home

A D/A D/G | A D/A D/G |
yeah.

Cmaj7 | E^7 |
Freedom of the papers, all you've got to do, oh

Fmaj7 | G |
no, no, oh

A D/A D/G | A D/A D/G |
no.

Interlude

E B9sus4 E B9sus4 E B9sus4 E B9sus4
| / / / / | / / / / | / / / / | / / / / |

E B9sus4 E B9sus4 E B9sus4 E B9sus4
| / / / / | / / / / | / / / / | / / / / |

A E B9sus4 E B9sus4
| / / / / | / / / / | / / / / | / / / / |

Cmaj7 E
| / / / / | / / / / |

Verse 4

A D/A D/G | A D/A D/G |
If you want to go out

A D/A D/G | A D/A D/G |
if you want to go out

Cmaj7 | E^7 |
Read it in the papers, tell me what it's all about

```
    A   D/A A/G  A   D/G A/G
  | / / /   /  | / / /   / |
```

Cmaj7 | E7 |
Read it in the papers, all you've got to do, oh

Fmaj7 | G |
no,   not

```
  A  D/A  D/G  | A  D/A  D/G  |
  me.
```

Coda
```
    A    D/A   D/G | A  D/A  D/G  |
    If you want to go     out
```

```
    A    D/A   D/G | A  D/A  D/G  |
    If you want to go     out
```

```
     A   D/A D/G  A   D/A D/G  A   D/A D/G  A   D/A D/G
   | / / /   /  | / / /     / | / / /   / | / / /     / |
```

```
     A   G/A  A   G/A  A   G/A  A   G/A  (repeat to fade)
   | / / / / | / / / / | / / / / | / / / / |
```

In It For The Money

Words and Music by
GARETH COOMBES, MICHAEL QUINN, DANIEL GOFFEY AND ROBERT COOMBES

Chord diagrams: E♭dim, D7, E7(♯5), Am, A♭7(♭9), G6, A13, A7add4, D, Dsus4, F5, C, B7, B♭7, B♭, G7, D/F♯, C/E, E♭maj9, G7/D, F/C, F

♩ = 112

Intro

| E♭dim7 | D7 | E7♯5 | Am |

4/4 | / / / / | / / / / | / / / / | / / / / |

| E♭dim7 | D7 | E7♯5 | Am |

| / / / / | / / / / | / / / / | / / / / |

Verse

E♭dim | D7 | E7♯5 | Am |
Here   I see a time   to go

A7♭9 | D7 | E7♯5 | Am |
    and leave it all behind

E♭dim | D7 | E7♯5 | Am |
And you know it's wrong to fall

A7♭9 | D7 | E7♯5 G6 |
    We're

A7 | |
in it for the money, we're in it for the money, we're

A7♯5 | |
in it for the money, we're in it for the money, we're

A13 | |
in it for the money, we're in it for the money, we're

A7add4 | |
in it for the money, we're in it for the money. Got my

20

© 1996 EMI Music Publishing Ltd, London WC2H 0EA

Chorus 1

D   D^{sus4} D | F⁵   C |

mind made up, I got my finger on the button, going

B⁷ | F |

way   home,   got the

D | F   C |

sun turned down, got a feeling in my pocket, going

B⁷ | B♭⁷ | |

way home.   But

Interlude

D | C | B♭ | G⁷ |

all I can see is our love,   and all I can hear is her,   and

D/F♯ | C/E |

all I can see is our love,   and

E♭^{maj9} | G⁷/D | |

all I can hear is her.

D   F/C   C   B⁷   F

| / / / / / | / / / / / | / / / / / | / / / / / |

D | F/C   C | B⁷ | F |

Got my

Chorus 2

D   D^{sus4} D | F⁵   C |

mind made up, I got my finger on the button, going

B⁷ | F |

way   home,   got the

D | F   C |

sun turned down, got a feeling in my pocket, going

B⁷ | B♭⁷ | |

way home.   But

Chorus 3

D   D^{sus4} D | F⁵   C |

mind made up, I got my finger on the button, going

B⁷ | F |

way   home,   got the

D | F   C |

sun turned down, got a feeling in my pocket, going

B⁷ | B♭⁷ | ‖

way home.

It's Not Me

Words and Music by
GARETH COOMBES, MICHAEL QUINN, DANIEL GOFFEY and ROBERT COOMBES

Chord diagrams: F#m7 Badd9/F# D7 C#m11 G# F#/G# C#11 F#add9

F# F#6 Aadd9 F#/A# Emaj7 Badd9 F#/B F#maj7

①=E ④=E
②=B ⑤=A
③=G# ⑥=E
Capo on 2nd fret

♩ = 104

Intro

| F#m7 | Badd9/F# | D7 | C#m11 |
| 4/4 / / / / | / / / / | / / / / | / / / / |

| F#m7 | Badd9/F# | D7 | C#m11 |
| / / / / | / / / / | / / / / | / / / / |

Verse 1

F#m7 | Badd9/F# | D7 | C#m11 |

Over their heads I find a place to crawl away,

F#m7 | Badd9/F# | D7 | C#m11 |

so many times I hear the things we used to say.

G#   F#/G# G#   F#/G# C#11

| / / / / | / / / / | / / / / | / / / / |

Verse 2

F#m7 | Badd9/F# | D7 | C#m11 |

Into the night the conversation fades away,

F#m7 | Badd9/F# | D7 | C#m11 |

losing the drift of all the things I had to say

G#   F#/G# G#   F#/G# C#11

| / / / / | / / / / | / / / / | / / / / |

Chorus 1

F#add9   F# | D7 |

It's not me, no no not me but I

F#6   F# | Aadd9 |

don't know what is.   I

22

© 1996 EMI Music Publishing Ltd, London WC2H 0EA

F#add9   F# | D7 |
try and find my peace of mind   but I

F#6   F# | Aadd9 |
know what I miss,   now it's gone,

G#   F#/G# | G#   F#/G# | C#11 | |
now it's gone,   now it's gone.

Interlude   F#/A# | Emaj7 | G# | C#11 |
As everyone listened   my head turned away,

F#/A# | Emaj7 | G# |
I know what I'm missing,   I've nothing to say.

   C#11
| / / / / | / / / / |

Chorus 2   F#add9   F# | D7 |
It's not me, no no not me but I

F#6   F# | Aadd9 |
don't know what is.   I

F#add9   F# | D7 |
try and find my peace of mind   but I

F#6   F# | Aadd9 |
know what I miss.

Chorus 3   F#add9   F# | D7 |
It's not me, no no not me but I

F#6   F# | Aadd9 |
don't know what is.   I

F#add9   F# | D7 |
try and find my peace of mind   but I

F#6   F# | Aadd9 |
know what I miss.

   Badd9   F#/B Badd9   F#/B
| / / / / | / / / / |

   Badd9 F#/B Badd9 F#/B Badd9 F#/B Badd9 F#/B F#maj7
| / / / / | / / / / | / / / / ‖

Late In The Day

Words and Music by
GARETH COOMBES, MICHAEL QUINN, DANIEL GOFFEY AND ROBERT COOMBES

Dmaj7 Fmaj7 Am Am13 F Bb D A E7sus4/B

G13 A7(#5)/C# Em Em(add9) C F#7(#11) D7 Am7

♩ = 84

Intro

Dmaj7   Fmaj7   Am   Am13
4/4 | / / / / | / / / / | / / / / | / / / / |

F   Bb   F   Bb   F D   A
| / / / / | / / / / | 2/4 | / / | 4/4 | / / / / |

Verse 1

Dmaj7 | Fmaj7 |
It's late in the day, I'm thinking of you,

Am   Am13 | F   Bb |
    things that you say,   so

F   Bb | F   D | A |
long, so   long for   me.

Dmaj7 | Fmaj7 |
It's late in the day, I'm talking to you

Am   Am13 | F   Bb |
    hear what I say,   so

F   Bb | F   D | A | |
long, so   long for me

Chorus 1

                        | Fmaj7 |
And all the time I've thought of you

E7sus4/B | G13 |
in an ordinary way, we'd slip off down the oily way

A | Fmaj7 |
and all I really have to say

E7sus4/B | B7 |
is people pass along the way had thoughts of you and me again.

Verse 2

D^{maj7} | F^{maj7} |
I lay on my bed   searching my mind,

Am   Am¹³ | F   B♭ |
        lighten my load,   so

F   B♭ | F   D | A |
long, so   long for me.

D^{maj7} | F^{maj7} |
I sleep on the road, and dream of a sound,

Am   Am¹³ | F   B♭ |
        coming my way,   so

F   B♭ | F   D | A | |
long, so   long for me.

Chorus 2
                                        | F^{maj7} |
And all the time I've thought of you

E^{7sus4}/B | G¹³ |
in an ordinary way,   we'd slip off down the oily way

A | F^{maj7} |
and all I really have to say

E^{7sus4}/B | B⁷ |
is people pass along the way   had thoughts of you and me again.

Interlude

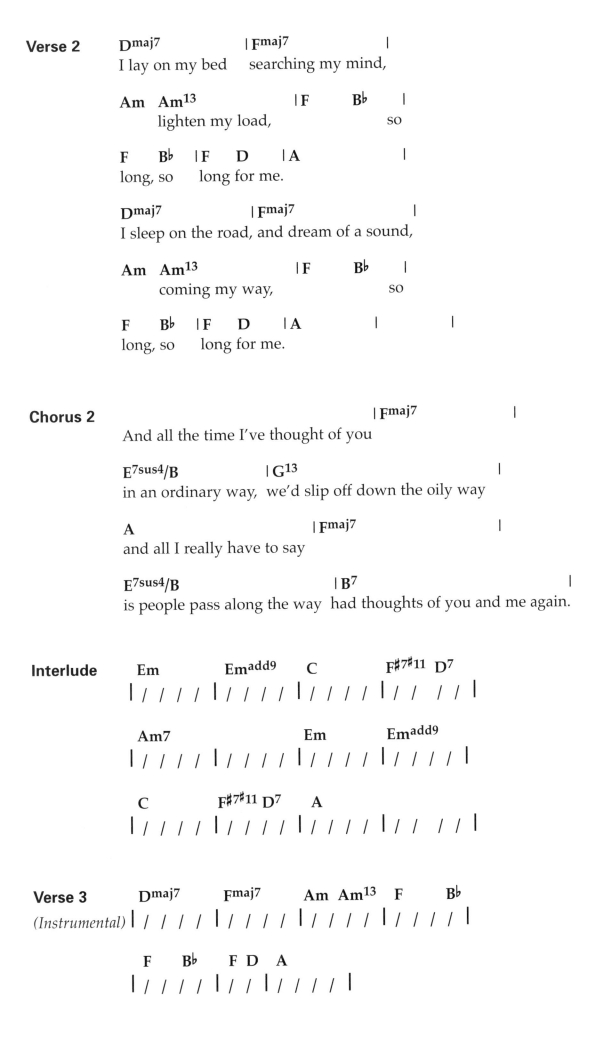

Verse 3
(Instrumental)

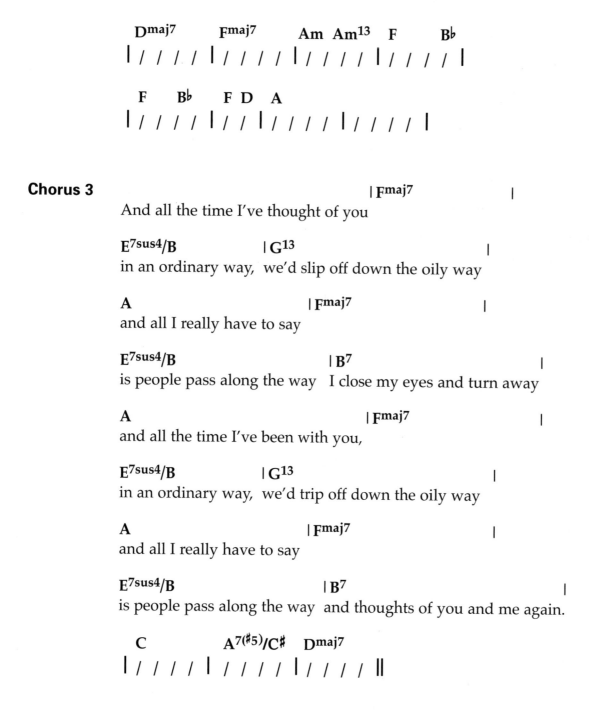

D^maj7   F^maj7   Am Am^13   F   B♭

| / / / / / | / / / / / | / / / / / | / / / / / |

F   B♭   F D   A

| / / / / / | / / / | / / / / / | / / / / / |

Chorus 3

| F^maj7 |
And all the time I've thought of you

E^7sus4/B | G^13 |
in an ordinary way, we'd slip off down the oily way

A | F^maj7 |
and all I really have to say

E^7sus4/B | B^7 |
is people pass along the way I close my eyes and turn away

A | F^maj7 |
and all the time I've been with you,

E^7sus4/B | G^13 |
in an ordinary way, we'd trip off down the oily way

A | F^maj7 |
and all I really have to say

E^7sus4/B | B^7 |
is people pass along the way and thoughts of you and me again.

C   A^7(♯5)/C♯   D^maj7

| / / / / / | / / / / / | / / / / / ‖

Pumping On Your Stereo

Words and Music by
GARETH COOMBES, MICHAEL QUINN, DANIEL GOFFEY AND ROBERT COOMBES

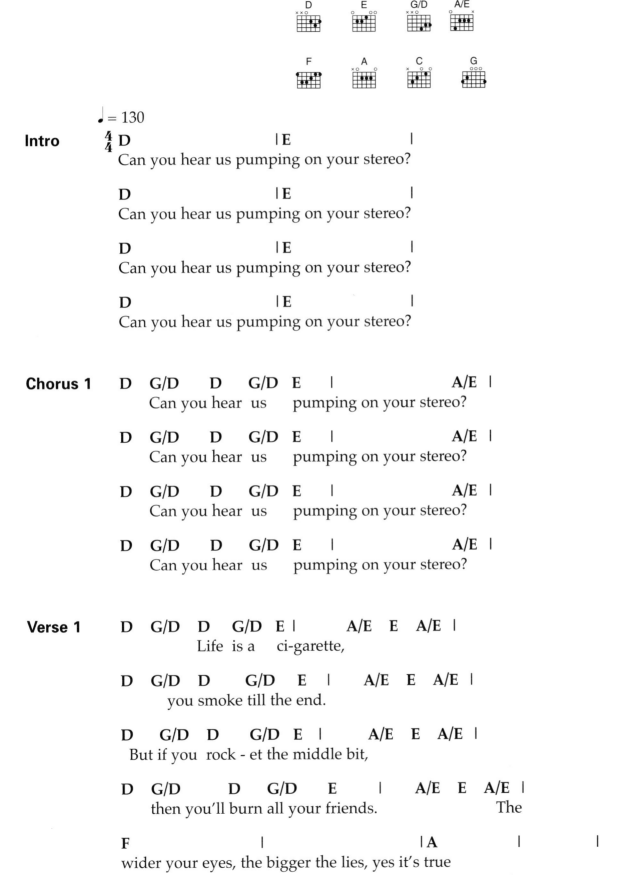

Intro   ♩ = 130

4/4 D | E |
Can you hear us pumping on your stereo?

D | E |
Can you hear us pumping on your stereo?

D | E |
Can you hear us pumping on your stereo?

D | E |
Can you hear us pumping on your stereo?

Chorus 1   D   G/D   D   G/D   E | A/E |
Can you hear us   pumping on your stereo?

D   G/D   D   G/D   E | A/E |
Can you hear us   pumping on your stereo?

D   G/D   D   G/D   E | A/E |
Can you hear us   pumping on your stereo?

D   G/D   D   G/D   E | A/E |
Can you hear us   pumping on your stereo?

Verse 1   D   G/D   D   G/D   E | A/E   E   A/E |
Life is a   ci-garette,

D   G/D   D   G/D   E | A/E   E   A/E |
you smoke till the end.

D   G/D   D   G/D   E | A/E   E   A/E |
But if you rock - et the middle bit,

D   G/D   D   G/D   E | A/E   E   A/E |
then you'll burn all your friends.   The

F | |A | |
wider your eyes, the bigger the lies, yes it's true

Chorus 2 D G/D   D   G/D E | A/E |
Can you hear us   pumping on your stereo?

D   G/D   D   G/D E | A/E |
Can you hear us   pumping on your stereo?

Verse 2 D   G/D   D   G/D   E | A/E   E   A/E |
Take a look through your window now,

D   G/D D G/D E | A/E   E   A/E |
you're all a - lone on the road.

D   G/D   D   G/D E | A/E   E   A/E |
Well you'll burn all your bridges down

D   G/D   D   G/D E | A/E   E   A/E |
and now you're los - ing control.   The

F | |A | |
wider your eyes, the bigger the lies, yes it's true.   If you make

C | |
a mistake where you couldn't relate to your groove.

G | |
That's true.

Chorus 3 D   G/D   D   G/D E | A/E |
Can you hear us   pumping on your stereo?

D   G/D   D   G/D E | A/E |
Can you hear us   pumping on your stereo?

D   G/D   D   G/D E | A/E |
Can you hear us   pumping on your stereo?

D   G/D   D   G/D E | A/E |
Can you hear us   pumping on your stereo?

Verse 3 D   G/D D   G/D   E | A/E   E   A/E |
Well now that I've met you,

D   G/D D G/D   E | A/E   E   A/E |
and I love you as a friend.

D   G/D   D   G/D E | A/E   E   A/E |
Yeah but your love is mogadon.

D   G/D D   G/D E | A/E   E   A/E |
love is the   end.   Well, the

28

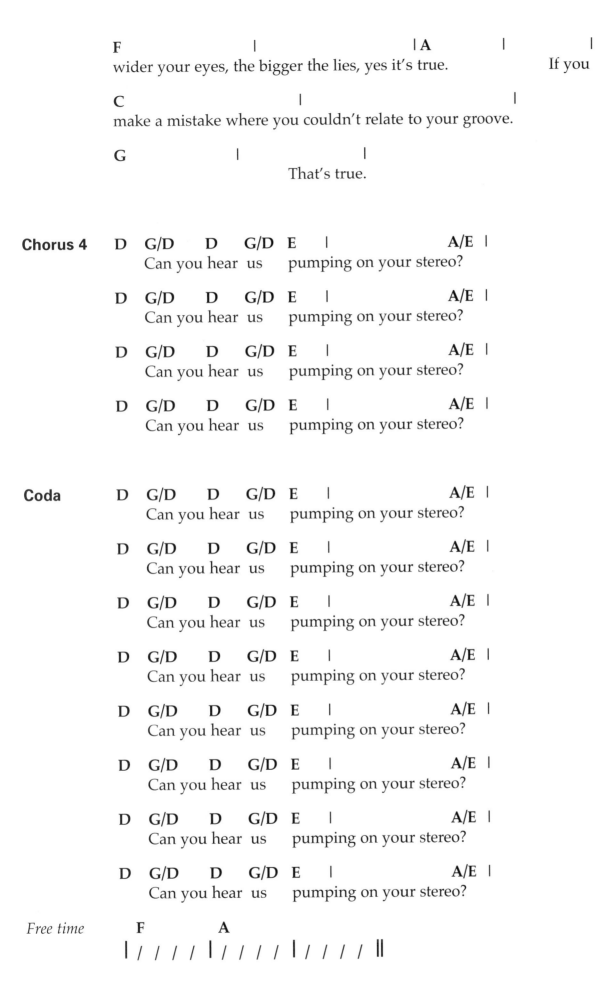

F | | **A** | |
wider your eyes, the bigger the lies, yes it's true.   If you

C | |
make a mistake where you couldn't relate to your groove.

G | |
             That's true.

Chorus 4   D   G/D   D   G/D   E | A/E |
                Can you hear us   pumping on your stereo?

                 D   G/D   D   G/D   E | A/E |
                Can you hear us   pumping on your stereo?

                 D   G/D   D   G/D   E | A/E |
                Can you hear us   pumping on your stereo?

                 D   G/D   D   G/D   E | A/E |
                Can you hear us   pumping on your stereo?

Coda   D   G/D   D   G/D   E | A/E |
                Can you hear us   pumping on your stereo?

                 D   G/D   D   G/D   E | A/E |
                Can you hear us   pumping on your stereo?

                 D   G/D   D   G/D   E | A/E |
                Can you hear us   pumping on your stereo?

                 D   G/D   D   G/D   E | A/E |
                Can you hear us   pumping on your stereo?

                 D   G/D   D   G/D   E | A/E |
                Can you hear us   pumping on your stereo?

                 D   G/D   D   G/D   E | A/E |
                Can you hear us   pumping on your stereo?

                 D   G/D   D   G/D   E | A/E |
                Can you hear us   pumping on your stereo?

Free time   **F**   **A**

| / / / / / | / / / / / | / / / / / ‖

Lenny

Words and Music by
GARETH COOMBES, MICHAEL QUINN AND DANIEL GOFFEY

E   B   B♭add9/F   F

A   G♯   G   F♯

♩ = 152

Intro

E   *repeat seven times*

4/4 ‖: / / / / | / / / / :‖ / / / / |

I've been a-

Verse 1

E | | | |
round and around, but I've got nowhere to go now,   but the

                    | | | |
funny thing is, that when I'm gone I'll kill you.

Chorus 1

B | | | |
When I tell you   I don't want you-hoo-

E | | | |
hoo.   I've been a-

Verse 2

                    | | | |
round and around, but I've got nowhere to go now,   but the

                    | | | |
funny thing is, that when I'm gone I'll kill you.

Chorus 2

B | | | |
When I tell you   I don't want you-hoo-

E | | | |
hoo.   I've been a-

Interlude **B♭add9/F** **F** | |**B♭add9/F** **F** | **B** |
Ahhh yeah.

| / / / / | / / / / | / / / / | / / / / |

B♭add9/F **F** | |**B♭add9/F** **F** | **B** |
Ahhh yeah.

| / / / / | / / / / | / / / / | / / / / |

B♭add9/F **F** | |**B♭add9/F** **F** | **B** |
Ahhh yeah.

                                             E

| / / / / | / / / / | / / / / | / / / / | |

| / / / / | / / / / | / / / / | / / / / |

| / / / / | / / / / | / / / / | / / / / |

| / / / / | / / / / | / / / / |

|
I've been a-

Verse 3

                       | | | |
round and around, but I've got nowhere to go now, but the

               | | | |
funny thing is, that when I'm gone I'll kill you.

Chorus 3 **B** | | | |
When I tell you I don't want you-hoo-

E | | | ‖
hoo.

Man Size Rooster

Words and Music by
GARETH COOMBES, MICHAEL QUINN AND DANIEL GOFFEY

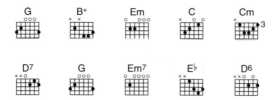

$\rule{0pt}{0pt} = 168$

Intro

G   B+   Em   B+   G   B+   Em   B+

4/4 | / / / / | / / / / | / / / / | / / / / |

Verse 1

G   B+ | Em   B+ |
Wait a minute now, you can't just run away,

G   B+ | Em   B+ |
You've got no money, and you've got no place to stay.

G   B+ | Em   B+ |
Things are bad, but there's always another way.

G | |
How would you know if you never ever saw me?

Chorus 1

C | | Cm | |
Oh no, when I look at you I see.

D⁷ | | | |
Why you lookin' so crazy?   Why you lookin' so lonely for love?

G | | Em⁷ | |
What do you wanna be now?

D⁷ | | | |
Why you lookin' so crazy?   Why you lookin' so lonely for love?

G | | Em⁷ | |
What do you wanna see now?

D⁷ | | | |
Wait a minute, it's all wrong. Wait a minute, it's all gone

G   B+ | Em   B+ | G   B+ | Em   B+ |
wrong.   *A rooster.*

Verse 2   G   B+ | Em   B+ |
Wait a minute now, you can't just hide away,

                 G   B+ | Em   B+ |
you've got no money, and you've got no face to save.

                 G   B+ | Em   B+ |
You think it's bad, but there's always another way.

                 G | |
How would you know if you never ever saw me?

Chorus 2   C | | Cm | |
Oh no, when I look at you I see.

                 D^7 | | | |
Why you lookin' so crazy?   Why you lookin' so lonely for love?

                 G | | Em^7 | |
                  What do you wanna be now?

                 D^7 | | | |
Why you lookin' so crazy?   Why you lookin' so lonely for love?

                 G | | Em^7 | $E^\flat$ |
                  What do you wanna be now?   *Oh*

                 G | | Em^7 | $E^\flat$ |
yeah.   What do you wanna see?   *Oh*

                 G | | Em^7 | $E^\flat$ |
yeah.   What do you wanna be?   *Oh*

                 G | | Em^7 |
yeah.   What do you wanna feel?

Coda $\frac{9}{8}$ D^6 G D^6 G D^6 G |
             Oh

             $\frac{4}{4}$ G | | Em^7 | $\frac{9}{8}$ D^6 G D^6 G D^6 G |
             yeah.

             (Repeat last 4 bars ad lib to fade)

Moving

Words and Music by
GARETH COOMBES, MICHAEL QUINN, DANIEL GOFFEY AND ROBERT COOMBES

Chord diagrams: $D^{13}sus4$, $Em(add9)$, $Csus2$, $Cadd9$, Am^7, $B^7sus2/F\sharp$

Chord diagrams: $B^7/F\sharp$, Bm, A, Em, B^7sus2, B^7

♩ = 110

Verse 1

$D^{13}sus4$ | | | |

4/4 Moving, just keep moving   till I don't know

Em^{add9} | | | |

why to stay.

C^{sus2} | C^{add9} | Am^7 | |

   I've been moving so long   the   days all feel the

$B^7sus2/F\sharp$ | | $B^7/F\sharp$ | |

same.

Verse 2

$D^{13}sus4$ | | | |

Moving, just keep moving,   well I don't know

Em^{add9} | | | |

why to stay.

C^{sus2} | C^{add9} | Am^7 | |

   And no ties to bind me,   no reasons to re-

$B^7sus2/F\sharp$ | | $B^7/F\sharp$ | N.C. |

main.   I've got a

Chorus 1

Bm   A | Em |

low, low, feeling around me   and a

Bm   A | Em |

stone cold feeling inside.   And I just

Bm   A | Em |

can't stop messing my mind up and wasting my

Bm   A | Em |

time.   Ooh.   There's a

Bm   A | Em |

low, low feeling around me   and a

Bm   **A** |**Em** |
stone cold feeling inside.   I've got to

Bm   **A** |**Em** |
find somebody to help me,   I'll keep you in

B^{7sus2} |**B**^{7} |
mind.   So I'll keep

Verse 3   **D**^{13sus4} | | | |
Moving, just keep moving,   well I don't know

           Em^{add9} | | | |
who I am.

           C^{sus2} |**C**^{add9} |**Am**^{7} | |
No lead to follow,   there's no way back a-

           B^{7sus2}**/F**♯ | |**B**^{7}**/F**♯ | |
gain.

Verse 4   **D**^{13sus4} | | | |
Moving, keep on moving,   well I feel I'm

           Em^{add9} | | | |
born again.

           C^{sus2} |**C**^{add9} |**Am**^{7} | |
And when it's over,   I'll see you a-

           B^{7sus2}**/F**♯ | | | |
gain.

           B^{7}**/F**♯   N.C.
| / / / / | / / / / |

Coda   **D**^{13sus4}
| / / / / | / / / / | / / / / | / / / / |

           Em^{add9}
| / / / / | / / / / | / / / / | / / / / |

           C^{sus2} **C**^{add9} **Am**^{7}
| / / / / | / / / / | / / / / | / / / / |

           B^{7sus2}**/F**♯   **B**^{7}**/F**♯   *(repeat Coda and fade)*
| / / / / | / / / / | / / / / | / / / / |

Richard III

Words and Music by
GARETH COOMBES, MICHAEL QUINN, DANIEL GOFFEY AND ROBERT COOMBES

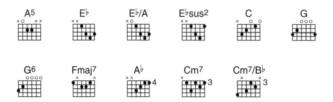

♩ = 152

Intro

   A⁵   E♭   A⁵   E♭/A

$\frac{4}{4}$ | / / / / | / / / / | / / / / | / / / / |

  A⁵   E♭/A C

| / / / / | / / / / | / / / / | / / / / |

  A⁵   E♭sus2 A⁵   E♭sus2

| / / / / | / / / / | / / / / | / / / / |

  A⁵   E♭sus2 A⁵

| / / / / | / / / / | / / / / |

E♭sus2 |
Got up today,

Verse 1 A⁵ |E♭sus2 |A⁵ |E♭sus2 |
       what a day, thanks a million,   I spend too much time

       A⁵ |E♭sus2 |A⁵ |E♭sus2 |
       wondering why I've got an opinion, yeah.

Chorus 1 C | |A♭ | |
       I know you want to try and get away,   but it's the

       G | |C | |
       hardest thing you'll ever know,

       A⁵ |E♭sus2 |A⁵ |E♭sus2 |
       yeah.   Waiting in line,

Verse 2
A⁵ |E♭sus2 |A⁵ |E♭sus2 |
terrible time, over familiar, we'll take them away,

A⁵ |E♭sus2 |A⁵ |E♭sus2 |
and not let them say, they're over the hill, yeah.

Chorus 2
C | |A♭ | |
I know you want to try and get away, but it's the

G | |C | |
hardest thing you'll ever know,

Interlude

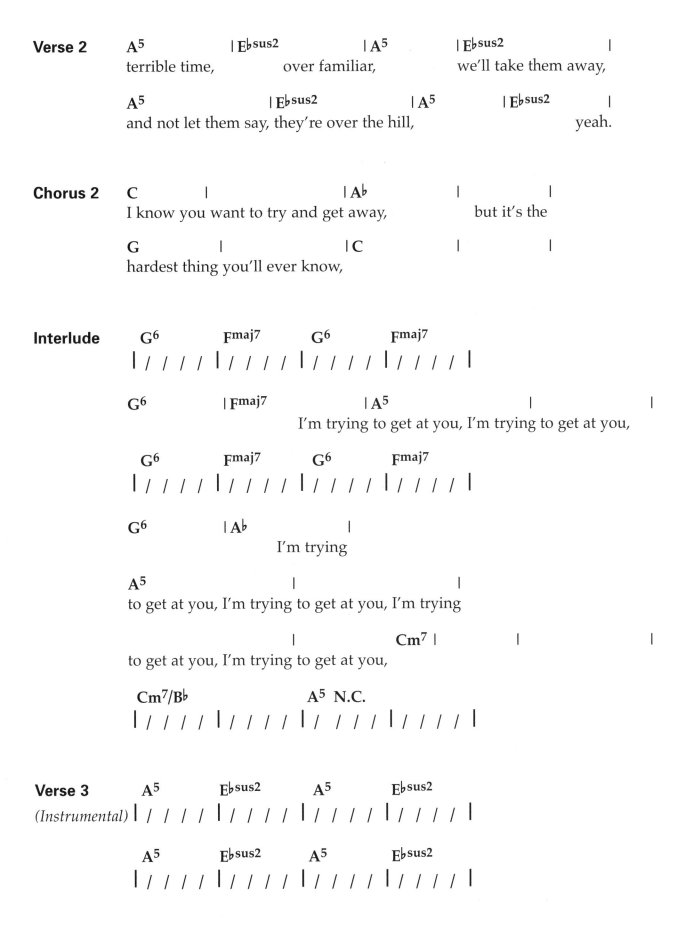

G⁶ Fmaj7 G⁶ Fmaj7

G⁶ |Fmaj7 |A⁵ | |
I'm trying to get at you, I'm trying to get at you,

G⁶ Fmaj7 G⁶ Fmaj7

G⁶ |A♭ |
I'm trying

A⁵ | |
to get at you, I'm trying to get at you, I'm trying

| Cm⁷ | | |
to get at you, I'm trying to get at you,

Cm⁷/B♭ A⁵ N.C.

Verse 3
(Instrumental)
A⁵ E♭sus2 A⁵ E♭sus2

A⁵ E♭sus2 A⁵ E♭sus2

Chorus 3   C | | A♭ | |

I know you want to try and get away,   but it's the

G | | C | |

hardest thing you'll ever know.

Chorus 4   C | | A♭   A♭sus4 | A♭   A♭sus4 |

I know you want to try and get away,   but it's the

G | | C | |

hardest thing you'll ever know.

| / / / / | / / / / | / / / / |

Coda   Cm⁷   Cm⁷/B♭   *(repeat Coda to fade)*

| / / / / | / / / / | / / / / | / / / / |

Sun Hits The Sky

Words and Music by
GARETH COOMBES, MICHAEL QUINN, DANIEL GOFFEY AND ROBERT COOMBES

Chord diagrams: F5 Eb5 Eb F Ebsus2 G Cm D

A Gm Am/D C C7sus4 Dsus4 D7

♩ = 150

Intro

| F5 | Eb5 | F5 | Eb5 |

4/4 | / / / / | / / / / | / / / / | / / / / |

| F5 | Eb5 | F5 | Eb5 |

| / / / / | / / / / | / / / / | / / / / |

Verse 1

F5 | Eb5 | F5 | Eb5 |

I know a place where the sun hits the sky,

F5 | Ebsus2 | F5 | Ebsus2 |

everything changes and blows out the night.

G | Cm | G | Cm |

Everyone knows why my tongue can't be tied,　　'cause

F5 | Ebsus2 | F5 | Ebsus2 |

I want to live where the sun meets the sky.

D 　　　A

| / / / / | / / / / |

Chorus 1

D | A | D | |

I am a doctor,　　　　I'll be your doctor,　　I'm on

Gm | | Am/D | |

my way　　and you won't come down today.

D | A | D | |

Live for the right things,　　　be with the right ones or they'll

Gm | | Am/D | |

hold you down, they'll turn your world around.

```
         F                        F5          Ebsus2
| / / / / / | / / / / / | / / / / / | / / / / |

  F5                  | Ebsus2                |
                                        Well,
```

Verse 2
```
  F5                | Eb5        | F5           | Eb5              |
I just don't know  why the sun  hits the sky,

  F5                | Ebsus2     | F5           | Ebsus2           |
everyone changed as they turned out the light.

  G        | Cm         | G            | Cm              |
Living is easy with time on my side,              'cause

  F5             | Ebsus2       | F5           | Ebsus2          |
I want to live  where the sun  meets the sky.

   D          A
| / / / / / | / / / / / |
```

Chorus 2
```
D        | A          | D            |                |
I am a doctor,        I'll be your doctor,    I'm on

Gm           |                    | Am/D          |              |
my way       and you won't come down today.

D            | A            | D            |              |
Live for the right things,     be with the right ones or they'll

Gm           |                    | Am/D          |              |
hold you down, they'll turn your world around.
```

Interlude
```
   Ab        Bb        F         Ebsus2
| / / / / / | / / / / / | / / / / / | / / / / / |

   Ab        Bb        F         G
| / / / / / | / / / / / | / / / / / | / / / / / |

   Ab        Bb        F         Ebsus2
| / / / / / | / / / / / | / / / / / | / / / / / |

   Ab        Bb        C         C7sus4  C
| / / / / / | / / / / / | / / / / / | / / / / / |
```

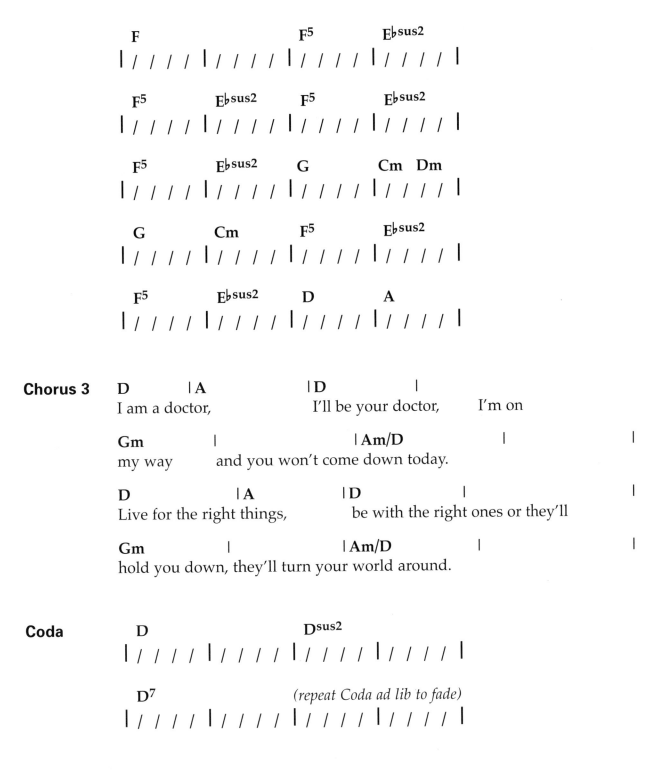

F   **F⁵**   **E♭sus2**

| / / / / | / / / / | / / / / | / / / / |

F⁵   **E♭sus2**   **F⁵**   **E♭sus2**

| / / / / | / / / / | / / / / | / / / / |

F⁵   **E♭sus2**   **G**   **Cm Dm**

| / / / / | / / / / | / / / / | / / / / |

G   **Cm**   **F⁵**   **E♭sus2**

| / / / / | / / / / | / / / / | / / / / |

F⁵   **E♭sus2**   **D**   **A**

| / / / / | / / / / | / / / / | / / / / |

Chorus 3   D | A | D |
I am a doctor,   I'll be your doctor,   I'm on

Gm | | Am/D | |
my way   and you won't come down today.

D | A | D | |
Live for the right things,   be with the right ones or they'll

Gm | | Am/D | |
hold you down, they'll turn your world around.

Coda   D   **Dsus2**

| / / / / | / / / / | / / / / | / / / / |

D⁷   *(repeat Coda ad lib to fade)*

| / / / / | / / / / | / / / / | / / / / |

Sitting Up Straight

Words and Music by
GARETH COOMBES, MICHAEL QUINN AND DANIEL GOFFEY

Chord diagrams: G, G/F, Em, E♭, Em7, Am, F/C, D

Chord diagrams: F#7, Bm, A7sus4, A7, C, B♭, G7, A

♩ = 156

Intro
```
        G    G/F  G    G/F  G    G/F  G    G/F
4/4 | / / / / | / / / / | / / / / | / / / / |
```

Chorus 1

G   G/F |
Sitting up straight on the back of the bus,

G   G/F |
mimicking time as the evening turns to

Em   **E♭** | |
dusk,   well

G   Em7 |
look at the boy with his face to the floor.

G   Em7 |
Have a little smoke just to pass the time of day,

Am   **F/C** | |G | |
oh   yeah,   oh yeah.

Verse 1

D   F#7   Bm |D |G |A7sus4   A7 |
He's like me, he'd do   anything to   get away, I know.

D   F#7   Bm |D |G |A7sus4   A7 |
Can   you be there   every day?   I know I can believe

D   F#7   Bm |D |G |Em7 |
in   you, it means   everything and every power to me.

```
    Am        C          D
| / / / / / | / / / / / | / / / / / | / / / / / |
```

```
    D  C    D  C    D  C    D  C
| / / / / / | / / / / / | / / / / / | / / / / / |
```

Chorus 2

D   C |
Sitting up straight on the back of the bus,

D   C |
mimicking time as the evening turns to

Bm   B♭ | |
dusk,   well

D   Bm |
look at the boy with his face to the floor.

D   Bm |
Have a little smoke just to pass the time of day,

Em   G | |D | |
      hey hey,   hey hey.

Verse 2

D   F♯7   Bm |D |G |A7sus4   A7 |
He's like me, he'd do   anything to   get away, I know.

D   F♯7   Bm |D |G |A7sus4   A7 |
Can you be there   every day? I know I can believe

D   F♯7   Bm |D |G |G7 |
in   you, it means   everything and every power to me.

A | |
           yeah, nice sound.

Interlude   D

| / / / / / | / / / / / | / / / / / | / / / / / |

| / / / / / | / / / / / | / / / / / | / / / / / | / / / / / | / / / / / |

Coda

                      | |D   C |
Sitting up straight, sitting up straight, sitting up

D   C |D   C |D   C |
straight, sitting up straight, sitting up straight on the back of a bus

D   C |D   C |
   on the back of a bus,   on the back of a bus

D   C |D   C |
   on the back of a bus,   on the back of a bus.

    D

| / / / / / ‖

Time To Go

Words and Music by
GARETH COOMBES, MICHAEL QUINN AND DANIEL GOFFEY

Fmaj7/C   Fmaj7/G   F#7/C#

Gadd6/D   Gadd6/A   F#7/G#

♩. = 106

Intro

Fmaj7/C   Fmaj7/G   Fmaj7/C   Fmaj7/G   Fmaj7/C   Fmaj7/G   Fmaj7/C   Fmaj7/G

12/8 | / / / / / / | / / / / / / | / / / / / / | / / / / / / |

Fmaj7/C   Fmaj7/G   Fmaj7/C   Fmaj7/G   Fmaj7/C   Fmaj7/G   Fmaj7/C   Fmaj7/G

| / / / / / / | / / / / / / | / / / / / / | / / / / / / |

Fmaj7/C   Fmaj7/G   Fmaj7/C   Fmaj7/G   Fmaj7/C   Fmaj7/G   Fmaj7/C   Fmaj7/G

| / / / / / / | / / / / / / | / / / / / / | / / / / / / |

Verse 1

Fmaj7/C   Fmaj7/G |Fmaj7/C   Fmaj7/G |
Thanks to everyone for everything you've done, but now it's

Fmaj7/C   Fmaj7/G |Fmaj7/C   Fmaj7/G |
time   to go.

Fmaj7/C   Fmaj7/G |
You know it's hard, we've had some

Fmaj7/C   Fmaj7/G |
fun, but now the moment's come, it's

Fmaj7/C   Fmaj7/G |Fmaj7/C   Fmaj7/G |
time   to go.

Chorus

Gadd6/D   Gadd6/A | F#7/C#   F#7/G# |
    Who could ask for more?

Fmaj7/C   Fmaj7/G   Fmaj7/C   Fmaj7/G

| / /   / / | / /   / / |

Fmaj7/C   Fmaj7/G   Fmaj7/C   Fmaj7/G

| / /   / / | / /   / / |

F^{maj7}/C   F^{maj7}/G   F^{maj7}/C   F^{maj7}/G

| / /   / / | / /   / / |

F^{maj7}/C   F^{maj7}/G   F^{#7}/C[#]

| / /   / / | / / / / |

G^{add6}/D   G^{add6}/A | F^{#7}/C[#]   F^{#7}/G[#] |

Who could ask for more?

Verse 2   F^{maj7}/C   F^{maj7}/G | F^{maj7}/C   F^{maj7}/G |

Thanks to everyone for everything you've done, but now it's

F^{maj7}/C   F^{maj7}/G | F^{maj7}/C   F^{maj7}/G |

time   to go.

F^{maj7}/C   F^{maj7}/G |

You know it's hard, we've had some

F^{maj7}/C   F^{maj7}/G |

fun, but now the moment's come, it's

F^{maj7}/C   F^{maj7}/G | F^{maj7}/C   F^{maj7}/G |

time   to go.

Coda   G^{add6}/D   G^{add6}/A | F^{#7}/C[#]   F^{#7}/G[#] |

Who could ask for more?

F^{maj7}/C   F^{maj7}/G   F^{maj7}/C   F^{maj7}/G   F^{maj7}/C

| / /   / / | / /   / / | / / / /   ‖

You Can See Me

Words and Music by
GARETH COOMBES, MICHAEL QUINN, DANIEL GOFFEY AND ROBERT COOMBES

Am   Dm   Fmaj7(♯11)   C   G7   E7/G♯   Am7

G   Gadd♯11   Gsus4   F   Em   Em7

♩ = 116

Intro   Am

$\frac{4}{4}$ | / / / / | / / / / | / / / / | / / / / |

Verse 1 | | Dm | |

If you like me, you can buy me and take me home,

Fmaj7(♯11) | C | G7 | E7/G♯ |

you can see me on your TV,   I'm alone,

Am | Am7 | Dm | |

you can call me, tell your story on the phone,

Fmaj7(♯11) | C | G7 | |

you can hear me over blue seas, I'm alone.

Chorus 1   G | Gadd♯11 | Gsus4 | F |

You can't see me I'm not really there,

Em | Gsus4 |

you can't see me I'm not really there.

      F   Em7

| / / / / | / / / / | / / / / |

Verse 2 | | Dm | |

When you need me, come and see me and take me out,

Fmaj7(♯11) | C | G7 | E7/G♯ |

in the evening, when we're sleepy, lay me down,

Am | Am7 | Dm | |
all the crazies, try and space me, and I don't know,

Fmaj7(♯11) | C | G7 | |
I'm not easy, don't try to please me, xenophobe.

Chorus 2

G | Gadd♯11 | Gsus4 | F |
You can't see me I'm not really there,

Em | Gsus4 |
you can't see me I'm not really there.

F Em7
| / / / / | / / / / | / / / / |

Interlude

Em
| / / / / | / / / / | / / / / | / / / / |

| / / / / | / / / / | / / / / | / / / / |

Am
| / / / / | / / / / |

Verse 3

| | Dm | |
If you like me, you can buy me and take me home,

Fmaj7(♯11) | C | G7 | E7/G♯ |
you can see me on your TV, I'm alone,

Am | Am7 | Dm | |
you can call me, tell your story on the phone,

Fmaj7(♯11) | C | G7 | |
you can hear me over blue seas, I'm alone.

Chorus 3

G | Gadd♯11 | Gsus4 | F |
You can't see me I'm not really there,

Em | Gsus4 |
you can't see me I'm not really there.

F Em7
| / / / / | / / / / | / / / / |

Chorus 4   G | G^{add#11} | G^{sus4} | F |

You can't see me I'm not really there,

Em | G^{sus4} |

you can't see me I'm not really there.

    F   Em⁷

| / / / / | / / / / | / / / / |

Coda   Am   *(repeat Coda and fade)*

| / / / / | / / / / | / / / / | / / / / |

Printed in England by Halstan & Co. Ltd., Amersham, Bucks.